The Chord Songbook

pulp

Wise Publications
London/New York/Paris/Sydney/Copenhagen/Madrid

Exclusive Distributors:
Music Sales Limited
8/9 Frith Street,
London W1V 5TZ, England.
Music Sales Pty Limited
120 Rothschild Avenue,
Rosebery, NSW 2018, Australia.

Order No. AM942678
ISBN 0-7119-6393-2
This book © Copyright 1997 by Wise Publications

Compiled by Peter Evans
Music arranged by Arthur Dick
Music processed by The Pitts

Cover design by Pearce Marchbank, Studio Twenty
Cover illustration by Pearce Marchbank
based on a photograph by Stefan DeBatselier/LFI

Your Guarantee of Quality
As publishers, we strive to produce every book
to the highest commercial standards.
This book has been carefully designed to minimise awkward
page turns and to make playing from it a real pleasure.
Particular care has been given to specifying acid-free,
neutral-sized paper made from pulps which have not been
elemental chlorine bleached. This pulp is from farmed sustainable
forests and was produced with special regard for the environment.
Throughout, the printing and binding have been planned to
ensure a sturdy, attractive publication which should give years
of enjoyment. If your copy fails to meet our high standards,
please inform us and we will gladly replace it.

Music Sales' complete catalogue describes thousands
of titles and is available in full colour sections by subject,
direct from Music Sales Limited. Please state your areas of interest
and send a cheque/postal order for £1.50 for postage to:
Music Sales Limited, Newmarket Road,
Bury St. Edmunds, Suffolk IP33 3YB.

Visit the Internet Music Shop at
http://www.musicsales.co.uk

Relative Tuning

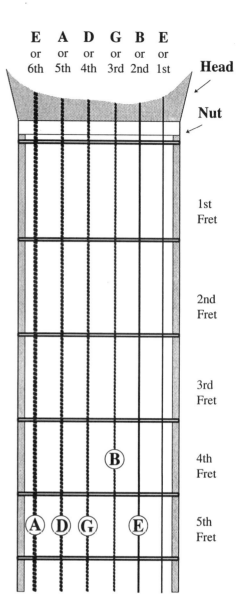

The guitar can be tuned with the aid of pitch pipes or dedicated electronic guitar tuners which are available through your local music dealer. If you do not have a tuning device, you can use relative tuning. Estimate the pitch of the 6th string as near as possible to E or at least a comfortable pitch (not too high, as you might break other strings in tuning up). Then, while checking the various positions on the diagram, place a finger from your left hand on the:

5th fret of the E or 6th string and **tune the open A** (or 5th string) to the note (A)

5th fret of the A or 5th string and **tune the open D** (or 4th string) to the note (D)

5th fret of the D or 4th string and **tune the open G** (or 3rd string) to the note (G)

4th fret of the G or 3rd string and **tune the open B** (or 2nd string) to the note (B)

5th fret of the B or 2nd string and **tune the open E** (or 1st string) to the note (E)

Reading Chord Boxes

Chord boxes are diagrams of the guitar neck viewed head upwards, face on as illustrated. The top horizontal line is the nut, unless a higher fret number is indicated, the others are the frets.

The vertical lines are the strings, starting from E (or 6th) on the left to E (or 1st) on the right.

The black dots indicate where to place your fingers.

Strings marked with an O are played open, not fretted.

Strings marked with an X should not be played.

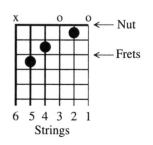

Babies

Music by Pulp
Lyrics by Jarvis Cocker

Dmaj7	G	Em	G2	A6

Intro   ‖: Dmaj7 | Dmaj7 | G | G :‖   *Play 6 times*

Verse 1

Dmaj7   G
Well, it happened years ago

Dmaj7   G
When you lived on Stanhope Road.

           Dmaj7
We listened to your sister

             G
When she came home from school,

          Dmaj7
'Cos she was two years older

        G
And she had boys in her room.

We listened outside and heard her, alright.

| Dmaj7 | Dmaj7 | G | G ‖

Verse 2

Dmaj7   G
Well, that was alright for a while,

         Dmaj7
But soon I wanted more.

        G
I wanna see as well as hear and so I,

        Dmaj7
I hid inside her wardrobe.

        G
And she came home round four,

          Dmaj7
And she was with some kid called David

       G
From the garage up the road.

I listened outside, I heard her, alright.

Chorus 1

Em   G2
Oh, I wanna take you home,

                  Dmaj7
I wanna give you children,

               G
You might be my girlfriend,

                      Dmaj7 G
Yeah, yeah, yeah, yeah, yeah, yeah.

Verse 3

Dmaj7   G
When I saw you next day

               Dmaj7
I really couldn't tell,

                          G
'Cos you might go and tell your mother.

                 Dmaj7
And so you went with Neve,

                     G
Oh yeah, and Neve was coming on

                    Dmaj7
And I thought I heard you laughing

                    G
When his mum and dad were gone.

I listened outside, I heard you, alright.

Chorus 2

Em   G2
Oh, I wanna take you home,

                  Dmaj7
I wanna give you children,

               G
You might be my girlfriend,

                      Dmaj7 G
Yeah, yeah, yeah, yeah, yeah, yeah

      Dmaj7   G
Oh, yeah.

Verse 4

             Dmaj7   G
Oh, well I guess it couldn't last too long,

             Dmaj7   G
I came home one day and all her things were gone.

               Dmaj7   G
I fell asleep inside, I never heard her come,

                        Dmaj7
Oh, and I opened up the wardrobe

                  G
And I had to get it on, yeah.

Dmaj⁷
Oh, listen we were on the bed when you came home,

G
I heard you stop outside the door,

Dmaj⁷
I know you won't believe it's true,

G
I only went with her'cos she looks like you.

Chorus 3

Em   **G²**
  Oh, I wanna take you home,

           Dmaj⁷
I wanna give you children,

           G
You might be my girlfriend,

                         A⁶   **G²**
Yeah, yeah, yeah, yeah, yeah, _____ oh, _____

                           Dmaj⁷
Yeah, yeah, yeah, yeah, yeah, yeah,

                           G
Yeah, yeah, yeah, yeah, yeah, yeah.

                           Dmaj⁷
Yeah, yeah, yeah, yeah, yeah, yeah,

                           G
Yeah, yeah, yeah, yeah, yeah, yeah.

Dmaj⁷
Yeah,

                           G
Yeah, yeah, yeah, yeah, yeah, yeah.

Dmaj⁷
Yeah,

                           G
Yeah, yeah, yeah, yeah, yeah, yeah.

Dmaj⁷
Yeah.

Bar Italia

Music by Pulp
Lyrics by Jarvis Cocker

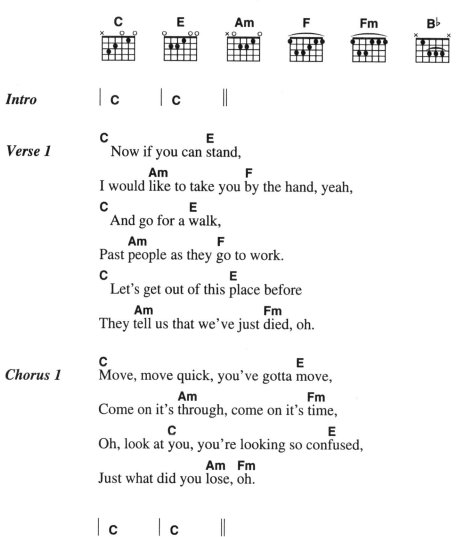

Intro | C | C ||

Verse 1

C   E
Now if you can stand,

    Am   F
I would like to take you by the hand, yeah,

C   E
And go for a walk,

    Am   F
Past people as they go to work.

C   E
Let's get out of this place before

    Am   Fm
They tell us that we've just died, oh.

Chorus 1

C   E
Move, move quick, you've gotta move,

      Am   Fm
Come on it's through, come on it's time,

         C   E
Oh, look at you, you're looking so confused,

       Am Fm
Just what did you lose, oh.

| C | C ||

Verse 2

   C   E
If you can make
    Am   F
An order, could you get me one?
   C   E
Two sugars would be great
     Am   F
'Cos I'm fading fast and it's nearly dawn.
   C   E
If they knocked down this place, this place,
     Am   Fm
It'd still look much better than you, oh now.

Chorus 2

As Chorus 1

   C
It's O.K. it's just your mind.

Instrumental

‖: C | E | Am | Fm   :‖

   C   E
If we get through this ali-hi-hive,
     Am   Fm
I'll meet you next week, same place, same time, oh.

Chorus 3

As Chorus 1

Outro

   C
That's what you get from clubbing it,
     E
You can't go home and go to bed
    Am
Because it hasn't worn off yet,
     Fm
And now it's morning.
       C
There's only one place we can go,
     E
It's around the corner in Soho
     Am   Fm
Where other broken people go.
B♭   C
Let's go.

Common People

Music by Pulp
Lyrics by Jarvis Cocker

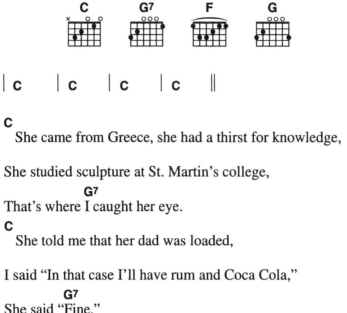

Intro | C | C | C | C ||

Verse 1
C
   She came from Greece, she had a thirst for knowledge,

She studied sculpture at St. Martin's college,
        G7
That's where I caught her eye.
C
   She told me that her dad was loaded,

I said "In that case I'll have rum and Coca Cola,"
      G7
She said "Fine."

And then in thirty seconds time she said
F
   "I want to live like common people,
                     C
I want to do whatever common people do,

Want to sleep with common people,
                     G
I want to sleep with common people like you."

Well, what else could I do?
                     C
I said, "I'll… I'll see what I can do."

Verse 2

(C)
I took her to a supermarket,

                                                  G
I don't know why but I had to start it somewhere, so it started there.

C
  I said "Pretend you've got no money,"

                                                G
She just laughed and said "Oh, you're so funny," I said "Yeah?

Well I can't see anyone else smiling in here,

                F
Are you sure you want to live like common people,

                                    C
You want to see whatever common people see,

You want to sleep with common people,

                                G
You want to sleep with common people like me?"

                                                C
But she didn't understand, she just smiled and held my hand.

Verse 3

Rent a flat above a shop, cut your hair and get a job,

          G7
Smoke some fags and play some pool, pretend you never went to school,

          C
But still you'll never get it right 'cause when you're laid in bed at night

          G7
Watching 'roaches climb the wall,

If you called your dad he could stop it all, yeah.

F
  You'll never live like common people,

                                    C
You'll never do whatever common people do.

You'll never fail like common people,

                                  G
You'll never watch your life slide out of view,

And then dance and drink and screw

                        C
Because there's nothing else to do.

Instrumental ‖: C | C | C | C | G | G | G | G :‖

Verse 4

F
Sing along with the common people,

C
Sing along and it might just get you through.

Laugh along with the common people,

G
Laugh along even though they're laughing at you,

And the stupid things that you do,

C
Because you think that poor is cool.

Verse 5

Like a dog lying in the corner,

They will bite you and never warn you,

G7
Look out, they'll tear your insides out,

C
'Cause everybody hates a tourist,

G7
Especially one who thinks it's all such a laugh,

And the chip stains and grease will come out in the bath.

F
You will never understand how it feels to live your life

C
With no meaning or control and with nowhere left to go.

G
You are amazed that they exist,

C
And they burn so bright whilst you can only wonder why.

Verse 6   As Verse 3

| C | C | C | C   ‖

(C)
‖: Want to live with common people like you. :‖ *Play 7 times*

‖: Oh, la, la, la, la. :‖   *Play 4 times*

Oh yeah.

Disco 2000

Music by Pulp
Lyrics by Jarvis Cocker

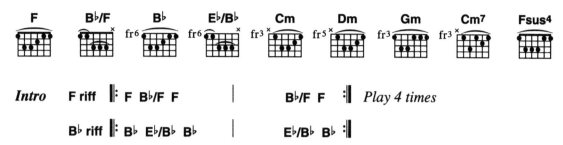

Intro   F riff ‖: F B♭/F F | B♭/F F :‖ *Play 4 times*

B♭ riff ‖: B♭ E♭/B♭ B♭ | E♭/B♭ B♭ :‖

Verse 1
>   **F riff**
> Oh, we were born within an hour of each other,
>
> Our mothers said we could be sister and brother,
>   **B♭ riff**
> Your name is De-bo-rah, Deborah,
>
> It never suited ya.
>   **F riff**
> And they said that when we grew up,
>
> We'd get married and never split up,
>   **B♭ riff**
> Oh, we never did it,
>
> Although I often thought of it.

Pre-chorus 1
>   **Cm**
> Oh, Deborah, do you recall?
>
> Your house was very small,
>
> With woodchip on the wall,
>
> When I came round to call
>   **F**
> You didn't notice me at all.

Chorus 1

        B♭
And I said "Let's all meet up in the year two thousand,

Dm   **Gm**
Won't it be strange when we're all fully grown,

                    Cm7   **Fsus4 F**
Be there two o'clock by the fountain down the road."_____

B♭
I never knew that you'd get married,

Dm   **Gm**
I would be living down here on my own,

                 Cm7   **Fsus4 F**
On that damp and lonely Thursday years ago. _____

Verse 2

    F riff
You were the first girl at school to get breasts,

And Martyn said that you were the best,

            B♭ riff
Oh, the boys all loved you but I was a mess,

I had to watch them trying to get you undressed.

             F riff
We were friends, _____ that was how it went,

I used to walk you home sometimes but it meant,

             B♭ riff
Oh, it meant nothing to you

'Cause you were so popular.

Pre-chorus 2   As Pre-chorus 1

Chorus 2   As Chorus 1

Instrumental ‖: F B♭/F F | B♭/F F :‖

                 ‖: B♭ E♭/B♭ B♭ | E♭/B♭ B♭ :‖

Pre-chorus 3

                       Cm
Oh, Deborah, do you recall?

Your house was very small,

With woodchip on the wall,

When I came round to call

                   F
You didn't notice me at all.

Chorus 3

                 B♭
And I said "Let's all meet up in the year two thousand,
Dm   **Gm**
Won't it be strange when we're all fully grown,
                    Cm⁷   **Fsus⁴** **F**
Be there two o'clock by the fountain down the road."_____
B♭
I never knew that you'd get married,
Dm   **Gm**
I would be living down here on my own,
                  Cm⁷   **Fsus⁴** **F**
On that damp and lonely Thursday years ago. _____

Outro

B♭
What are you doin' Sunday, baby?
Dm
Would you like to come and meet me, maybe?
Gm   **Cm⁷** **Fsus⁴** **F**
You can even bring your baby, ooh. _____
B♭
What are you doin' Sunday, baby?
Dm
Would you like to come and meet me, maybe?
Gm   **Cm⁷** **Fsus⁴**   **F**   **B**♭
You can even bring your baby, ooh, _____ ooh. _____

Do You Remember The First Time?

Music by Pulp
Lyrics by Jarvis Cocker

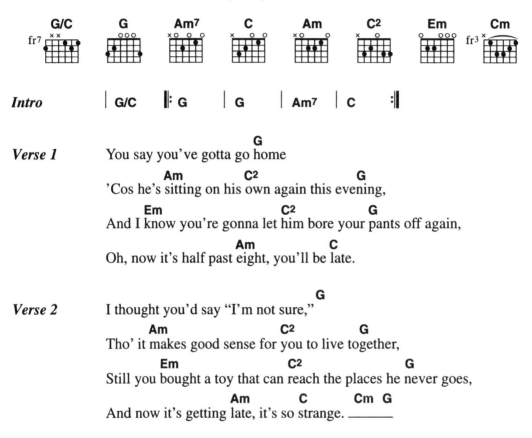

Intro | G/C ‖: G | G | Am7 | C :‖

Verse 1
                                                G
You say you've gotta go home
   Am   C2   G
'Cos he's sitting on his own again this evening,
    Em   C2   G
And I know you're gonna let him bore your pants off again,
                   Am   C
Oh, now it's half past eight, you'll be late.

Verse 2
                                                   G
I thought you'd say "I'm not sure,"
   Am   C2   G
Tho' it makes good sense for you to live together,
    Em   C2   G
Still you bought a toy that can reach the places he never goes,
                   Am   C   Cm G
And now it's getting late, it's so strange. _____

Chorus 1

G   Am⁷
 Do you remember the first time?

      C
I can't remember the worst time,

         Cm
Oh, but you know that we've changed so much since then,

      G
Oh yeah, we've grown.

          Am⁷
Now I don't care what you're doing,

       C
No, I don't care if you screw him,

        Cm
Ooh, just as long as you save a piece for me,

      G/C
Oh, yeah now, ooh.

Verse 3

       G
You wanna go home,

    Am   C2   G
Well at least there's someone there you can talk to,

    Em   C2   G
And you never have to face up to the night on your own,

       Am   C   Cm G
Jesus, it must be great to be straight. _____

Chorus 2   As Chorus 1

Interlude

(G/C)   G Am C
You wanna go home,

       G Am C
You wanna go home,

          G Am C
Oh yeah, you wanna go home,

       G Am C   G
You wanna go home.   Hey.

Chorus 3

(G)   Am⁷
  Do you remember the first time?

              C
I can't remember the worst time,

                  Cm
Oh, but you know that we've changed so much since then,

          G
Oh yeah, we've grown.

               Am⁷
Now I don't care what you're doing,

          C
No, I don't care if you screw him,

          Cm
Ooh, just as long as you save a piece for me,

Oh yeah, now.

Chorus 4

G   Am⁷
  Do you remember the first time?

           C
I can't remember the worst time,

                Cm
Oh, but you know that we've changed so much since then,

         G
Oh yeah, we've grown.

              Am⁷
Now I don't care what you're doing,

         C
No, I don't care if you screw him,

         Cm
Ooh, just as long as you save a piece for me,

       G/C
Oh, yeah now, ooh,

       G
You wanna go home.

Happy Endings

Music by Pulp
Lyrics by Jarvis Cocker

A   Amaj7   A7   D   A6   D7   Em7   Asus4   G

Intro

| A | A | Amaj7 | Amaj7 | A7 | A7 | D | D | |

| D | D | A6 | A6 | D7 | D7 | Em7 | A | ‖ |

Verse 1

A
Oh yeah, imagine it's a film and you're the star,

Amaj7
And pretty soon we're coming to the part

A7
Where you realise that you should give your heart,

D
Oh, give your heart to me.

And now the orchestra begins to make a sound

A6
That goes round and round and round and round

D7
And round and round and round,

Em7
And round and round again,

Asus4 A
And we kiss to violins.

Verse 2

          A
Well, some sad people might believe in that, I guess,

          Amaj7
Ah, but we know better, don't we?

We know all about the mess,

          A7
The aftermath of our affair is lying all around

          D
And I can't clear it away.

No, and do you think it's so easy to find

    A6
Somebody who is just your kind?

        D7
Oh, well it might take you a little time

         Em7
But I'm gonna have to try,

          A
Oh yeah, I'm gonna try. _____

Chorus 1

         D   **Em7**   **A**
And I know no one can ever know which way to head,

        Em7   **Asus4**
But don't you remember that you once said

      A   **D**   **A**
That you liked happy endings, happy endings?

    D   **Em7**   **A**
And no one can ever know if it's gonna work,

         Em7
But if you try, if you try,

Asus4   **A**   **D**
  Then you might get your happy ending.

Instrumental | A | A | Amaj7 | Amaj7 | A7 | A7 | D | D |

                    | D | D | A6 | A6 | D7 | D7 | Em7 | A ||

Chorus 2

                D   **Em⁷**   **A**
And I know no one can ever know which way to head,

             Em⁷   **G**
But don't you remember that you once said

                D   **A**
That you liked happy endings, happy endings?

        D   **Em⁷**   **A**
And no one can ever know if it's gonna work,

            Em⁷
And if you try, if you try

G   **D**
  Then you might get your happy ending,

              A
Your ending, that thing that you deserve.

Outro

                D   **Em⁷**   **A**
Oh, and no one can ever know which way to head,

                Em⁷   **G**
Ooh, but don't you remember that you once said

             D
You want happy endings?

Joyriders

Music by Pulp
Lyrics by Jarvis Cocker

C   G   Am   B7   F   Em   F#7   B

Verse 1

      C   G   Am
We like driving on a Saturday night,

      C   G   B7
Past the leisure centre, left at the lights.

                  C
Oh, we don't look for trouble

         F   Em
But if it comes we don't run,

             C
Looking out for trouble

       F   Em
Is what we call fun.

       B7
Hey you, you in the Jesus sandals,

      C   G   B7
Wouldn't you like to come over and watch some vandals

      C   G   B7
Smashing up someone's home?

Verse 2

      C   G   Am
We can't help it, we're so thick we can't think,

      C   G   B7
Can't think of anything but shit, sleep and drink.

              C
Oh, and we like women;

         F   Em
"Up the women," we say,

           C
And if we get lucky

             F   Em
We might even meet some one day.

       B7
Oh, you, you in the Jesus sandals,

      C   G   B7
Wouldn't you like to come over and watch some vandals

      C   G   B7
Smashing up someone's home?

Chorus 1

C   Em
Mister, we just want your car, _____

          C   Em
'Cos we're taking a girl to the reservoir, oh,

Am   F#7   B
All of the papers say it's a tragedy,

But don't you want to come and see?

Insrumental

| C | G   Am | C | G   B7 |

| C | F   Em | C | F   Em | B7 | B7 |

| C   G | B7 | B7 | C   G | B7 | B7 ||

Chorus 2

C   Em
Mister, we just want your car, _____

          C   Em
'Cos we're taking a girl to the reservoir, oh,

Am   F#7   B
All of the papers say it's a tragedy.

Chorus 3

C   Em
Mister, we just want your car, _____

          C   Em
'Cos we're taking a girl to the reservoir, oh,

Am   F#7   B
All of the papers say it's a tragedy,

But don't you want to come and see?

Chorus 4

C   Em
Mister, we just want your car, _____

          C   Em
'Cos we're taking a girl to the reservoir, oh,

Am   F#7   B
All of the papers say it's a tragedy.

I Spy

Music by Pulp
Lyrics by Jarvis Cocker

Cm   G7   Fm7   Gsus4   F/C

A♭/C   Am/C   G7/C   C#m   G#7   F#m7

Intro

      Cm   **G7**
   I spy a boy, I spy a girl,
  Cm   **G7**   **Cm**
I spy the worst place in the world, in the whole wide world.
      Fm7   **Cm**
Oh, you didn't do bad, you made it out,
      Fm7   **G7**   **Gsus4**   **Cm**
I'm still stuck here, oh, but I'll get out, oh yeah, I'll get out.

Verse 1

Can't you see a giant walks among you
            G7
Seeing through your pretty lives?
   Cm
Do you think I do these things for real?
          G7
I do these things just so I survive,
       Cm
And you know I will survive.
  Fm7
It may look to the untrained eye,
   Cm
I'm sitting on my arse all day,
  Fm7   **G7**
I'm biding time until I take you on,

My Lords and Ladies I will prevail,
        Cm
I cannot fail 'cause I spy.

Verse 2

(Cm)
Oh, I've got your number, taken notes,

                                      G7
And all the ways your minds work I've studied.

          Cm
Oh, and your minds are just the same as mine,

                       G7
Except that you're clever swines, you never let your masks slip,

                            Cm
You never admit to it, you're never hurried, oh, no, no, no.

        Fm7   **Cm**
And every night I hold my plan, how I will get my satisfaction,

        Fm7   **G7**   **Cm**
How I will blow your paradise away, away, away, ooh, 'cause I spy.

Middle
(spoken)

Cm
  It's just like in the old days,

F/C
I used to compose my own critical notices in my head.

A♭/C   **Am/C**
  The crowd gasp at Cocker's masterful control of the bicycle,

                                       A♭/C
Skillfully avoiding the dog turd outside the corner shop.

                         F/C   **G7**
Imagining a blue plaque above the place I first ever touched a girl's chest,

                         Cm
But hold on, you've got to wait for the best.

                                               F/C
You see, you should take me seriously, very seriously indeed,

                  A♭/C
'Cause I've been sleeping with your wife for the past sixteen weeks,

Am/C
  Smoking your cigarettes, drinking your brandy,

A♭/C
  Messing up the bed that you chose together.

F/C
  And in all that time I just wanted you to come home

G7   **Cm**
Unexpectedly one afternoon, and catch us at it in the front room.

                                        F/C
You see, I spy for a living and I specialise in revenge,

        A♭/C   **Am/C**
On taking the things I know will cause you pain. _____

                            A♭/C
I can't help it, I was dragged up, my favourite parks are car parks,

F/C   **G7/C**
  Grass is something you smoke, birds is something you shag,

                                     Cm
Take your "Year In Provence" and shove it up your arse.

Verse 3

   (Cm)   **G⁷**
Your Ladbroke Grove looks turn me on, yeah,

             Cm
With roach burns in designer dresses,

                   G⁷
Skin stretched tight over high cheek bones

And thousands of tiny dryness lines beating a path,

Cm
  Beating a path to the corners of your eyes.

     Fm⁷
And every night I hatch my plan,

     Cm
It's not a case of woman v. man,

     Fm⁷   **G⁷**
It's more a case of haves against haven'ts,

And I just happen to have got what you need,

                 Cm
Yeah, just exactly what you need, yeah.

Verse 4

C♯m
La, la, la, la, la, la, la, la,

G♯7
La, la, in the midnight hour,

C♯m
La, la, la, la, la, la, la, la,

G♯7
La, la, I will come to you,

C♯m
I will come to you.

F♯m⁷
I will take you from this sickness,

C♯m
Dinner parties and champagne,

    F♯m⁷   **G♯7**
I'll hold your body and make it sing again,

                                 Cm
Come on, sing again, let's sing again, oh yeah, 'cause I spy.

Outro

Yes, I spy, ssss.

            G⁷
I spy a boy, and I spy a girl,

   Cm   **G⁷**
I spy a chance to change the world,

   Cm
To change your world.

Lipgloss

Music by Pulp
Lyrics by Jarvis Cocker

Dm	C	G	F	Fm	G/B	Cmaj7

Intro ‖: Dm | Dm | C G | C G :‖

Verse 1

Dm
   No wonder you're looking thin,
      C   G
When all that you live on
   C   G
Is lipgloss and cigarettes,
Dm
   And scraps at the end of the day
         C   G
When he's given the rest
    C   G   Dm
To someone with long black hair. ____

All those nights in,
         C   G
Making such a mess of the bed,
      C   G   Dm
Oh, you never, ever want to go home.

And he wants you, so you may as well
      C   G
Hang around for a while,
     C   G
Call your dad on the phone.

Chorus 1

    F
    He changed his mind last Monday,

Fm   **C**
    So you've gotta leave by Sunday, yeah,

                        G/B   **C**
    Oh, you've lost your lipgloss, honey, oh yeah.

                  G/B   **F**
    Now nothing you do can turn him on,

    There's something wrong,

        Fm
    You had it once but now it's gone.

Verse 2

    Dm
    And you feel such a fool

    C   **G**
    For laughing at bad jokes,

    C   **G**   **Dm**
    And putting up with all of his friends,

    And kissing in public.

          C   **G**
    What are they gonna say

       C   **G**   **Dm**
    When they run into you again?

    That your stomach looks bigger,

         C   **G**
    And your hair is a mess,

         C   **G**   **Dm**
    And your eyes are just holes in your face. _____

    And it rains every day,

         C   **G**
    And when it doesn't, the sun

        C **G**
    Makes you feel worse anyway.

Chorus 2   As Chorus 1

Middle

G
  Though you knew

       Cmaj7   **F**   **G**
There was no way it was gonna last forever,

It still shook you,

       Cmaj7   **F**
When he told you in a letter

               Fm
That he didn't wanna see you,

             C
You nearly lost your mind, oh yeah.

Chorus 3

           G/B   **C**
Oh, you've lost your lipgloss, honey, oh yeah.

        G/B   **F**
Now nothing you do can turn him on,

There's something wrong,

   Fm
You had it once but now it's gone.

Chorus 4   As Chorus 3

Solo

C	C	G/B	G/B
C	C	G/B	F
F	Fm	Fm	C

Live Bed Show

Music by Pulp
Lyrics by Jarvis Cocker

Am   Esus4   E   Em   G   Dmaj7   D7   Fmaj7   F

Intro

        Am
She doesn't have to go to work

But she doesn't want to stay in bed,
        Esus4
'Cause it's changed from something comfortable
E   **Am**
  To something else instead.

Verse 1

          Em
This bed has seen it all from the first time to the last,
  G   **Dmaj7**
The silence of now and the good times of the past,
    D7   **G**
And it only cost ten pounds from a shop just down the road,
      Fmaj7   **E**   **Am**
Mind you that was seven years ago and things were very different then.

Verse 2

         Em
It didn't get much rest at first, the headboard banging in the night,
  G   **Dmaj7**
The neighbours didn't dare complain and everything was going right,
      D7   **G**
And now there's no need to complain 'cause it never makes a sound,
      Fmaj7   **E**   **Am**
Something beautiful left town, and she doesn't even know its name.

Middle

   F   **D7**
  Now ev'ry night she plays the sad game,
      F   **D7**
Ooh, called "pretending nothing's going wrong," ooh,
      G   **Fmaj7**
Oh, but she knows if this show was televised
        E
No one would watch it,
           Am
Not tonight but seven years ago.

Verse 3

(Am)
La, la, la, la, la, la,

Em
La, la, la, la, la, la, la, la,

G
La, la, la, la, la, la, la, la,

Dmaj⁷
La, la, la, la, la, la, la.

D⁷
Now there's no need to complain

G
'Cause it never makes a sound,

Fmaj⁷
Something beautiful left town

E   **Am**
And she never knew its name.

Outro

She doesn't have to go to work

But she doesn't want to stay in bed,

Em
'Cause it's changed from something comfortable

Am
To something else instead.

Mis-shapes

Music by Pulp
Lyrics by Jarvis Cocker

A   E   Fm   F#m   Dmaj7   D7   E7   G   Gaug

G6   G7   C   Caug   C6   C7   Em   C/E   Em6

Verse 1

A
Mis-shapes, mistakes, misfits,
E   Fm
Raised on a diet of broken biscuits, oh,
F#m
  We don't look the same as you,
Dmaj7
  And we don't do the things you do,
    D7
But we live 'round here too, oh really.

Verse 2

A
Mis-shapes, mistakes, misfits,
     E   Fm
We'd like to go to town but we can't risk it, oh,
F#m
  'Cause they just want to keep us out,
Dmaj7
  You could end up with a smack in the mouth
D7
Just for standing out, now really.

A   E7
  Brother, sisters, can't you see
         E   Fm F#m
The future's owned by you and me?
                Dmaj7
There won't be fighting in the street,

They think they've got us beat,
     D7   G
But revenge is going to be so sweet, oh. _____

Chorus 1

   (G)   **Gaug**   **G6**
We're making a move, we're making it now,

                         G7
We're coming out of the sidelines.

  C   **Caug**   **C6**
  Just put your hands up, it's a raid, yeah.

  C7   **Em**   **C/E**
  We want your homes, we want your lives,

               Em6   **C/E**
We want the things you won't allow us,

               Em   **C/E**
We won't use guns, we won't use bombs,

               Em6   **C/E**
We'll use the one thing we've got more of,

               Em
That's our minds.

        A
Verse 3   Check your lucky numbers,

    E   **Fm**
That much money could drag you under, oh,

F#m
  What's the point of being rich

Dmaj7
If you can't think what to do with it,

      D7
'Cause you're so bleeding thick.

   A   **E7**
  Oh, we weren't supposed to be,

            E
We learnt too much at school,

Fm **F#m**
Now we can't help but see

       Dmaj7
The future that you've got mapped out

   D7   **G**
Is nothing much to shout about, oh. ____

Chorus 2   As Chorus 1

Instrumental | E | E ||

              | A | A | E | E   Fm | F#m |

              | F#m | Dmaj7 | Dmaj7 | D7 | D7 ||

Verse 4

    A   **E⁷**
  And brother, sisters, can't you see

          E   **Fm F♯m**
The future's owned by you and me?

                    Dmaj⁷
There won't be fighting in the street,

They think that they've got us beat,

    D⁷   **G**
But revenge is going to be so sweet.

Chorus 2

           Gaug   **G⁶**
We're making a move, we're making it now,

        G⁷
We're coming out of the sidelines.

C   **Caug**   **C⁶**
  Just put your hands up, it's a raid, yeah.

C⁷   **Em**   **C/E**
  We want your homes, we want your lives,

      Em⁶   **C/E**
We want the things you won't allow us,

      Em   **C/E**
We won't use guns, we won't use bombs,

     Em⁶   **C/E**
We'll use the one thing we've got more of,

    Em   **C/E**   **Em⁶** **C/E**
That's our minds, ⸺⸺ yeah.

        Em   **C/E**   **Em⁶** **C/E** **A**
And that's our minds, ⸺⸺ yeah.

Monday Morning

Music by Pulp
Lyrics by Jarvis Cocker

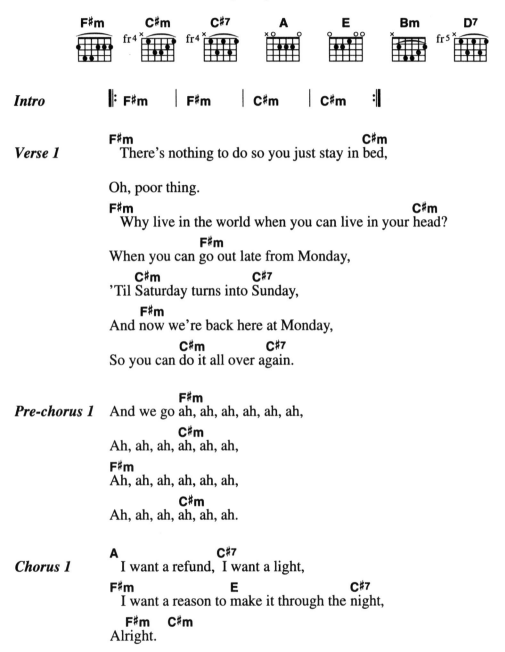

Intro ‖: F#m | F#m | C#m | C#m :‖

Verse 1
F#m   C#m
There's nothing to do so you just stay in bed,

Oh, poor thing.
F#m   C#m
Why live in the world when you can live in your head?
                        F#m
When you can go out late from Monday,
        C#m   C#7
'Til Saturday turns into Sunday,
        F#m
And now we're back here at Monday,
                C#m   C#7
So you can do it all over again.

Pre-chorus 1
                        F#m
And we go ah, ah, ah, ah, ah, ah,
                C#m
Ah, ah, ah, ah, ah, ah,
F#m
Ah, ah, ah, ah, ah, ah,
                C#m
Ah, ah, ah, ah, ah, ah.

Chorus 1
A   C#7
I want a refund, I want a light,
F#m   E   C#7
I want a reason to make it through the night,
        F#m   C#m
Alright.

Verse 2

F#m   C#m
And so you finally left school,

   C#7
So now what are you going to do?

F#m
Now you're so grown up, yeah,

C#m   C#7
Oh, oh, oh, oh, oh, so mature, oh.

F#m
Going out late from Monday,

   C#m   C#7
Ch-ch-chuck up in the street on Sunday,

F#m
You don't want to live till Monday,

   C#m   C#7
And gonna do it all over again.

Pre-chorus 2

      F#m
And we go ah, ah, ah, ah, ah, ah,

       C#m
Ah, ah, ah, ah, ah, ah,

F#m
Ah, ah, ah, ah, ah, ah,

       C#m
Ah, ah, ah, ah, ah, ah.

Chorus 2

A   C#7
I want a refund, I want a light,

F#m   E   C#7
I want a reason for all this night after night, after night,

After night, oh.

A
Oh, I know it's stupid,

   C#7   F#m
But I just can't seem to spend a night at home,

              E   C#7
'Cause my friends left town and I'm here all alone, oh.

F#m Bm
Yeah, they say the past must die,

F#m   Bm
For the future to be born, in that case die, die.

F#m Bm
Ooh, ooh,

F#m   D7 C#7
Ooh,

Stomach in, chest out, on your marks, get set, go!

Chorus 3

   A   C#7
   Now, now that you're free,

            F#m
What are you gonna be,

                 E   C#7
And who are you gonna see? _____

      A   C#7
And where will you go?

         F#m
And how will you know

               E   C#7
You didn't get it all wrong? _____

Chorus 4

    A
Is this the light of a new day dawning?

  C#7
A future bright that you can walk in?

F#m
No it's just another Monday morning,

E   C#7
Do it all over again, baby.

Outro

A   C#7
La, la, la, la, la, la,

               F#m
Ah, la, la, la, la, la,

          E   C#7
La, la, la, la, la, la, la, la, ow, ow, ow.

A   C#7
La, la, la, la, la, la,

               F#m
Ah, la, la, la, la, la,

          E   C#7
La, la, la, la, la, la, la, la, ow, ow, ow.

   A   C#7
Do, do, do, do, do, do, do, do, do,

              F#m
Do, do, do, do, do, do,

          E C#7
Do, do, do, do, do, do, do,

      A   C#7
Do, do, do, do, do, do, do, do, do,

              F#m
Do, do, do, do, do, do,

          E C#7   F#m
Do, do, do, do, do, do, do.

Pencil Skirt

Music by Pulp
Lyrics by Jarvis Cocker

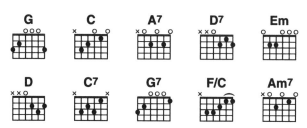

Verse 1

G C   A7
When you raise your pencil skirt

D7   G
Like a veil before my eyes,

C   A7
Like the look upon his face

D7   G
As he's zipping up his flies, oh.

C   A7   D7   G   C
Well I know that you're engaged to him, oh, ___

A7   D7   G
But I know you want something to play with, baby.

Chorus 1

Em
I'll be around when he's not in town, oh,

C
Yeah, I'll show you how you're doing it wrong, oh,

Em
I really love it when you tell me to stop, oh,

D   G
Oh, it's turning me on.

Verse 2

C   A7
Now you can tell some lies

D7   G
About the good times that you've had.

C   A7
I've kissed your mother twice

D7   G
And now I'm working on your dad, oh baby.

Chorus 2   As Chorus 1

Instrumental ‖: C7 | A7 D7 | G :‖

| Em | G7 | C | F/C C F/C C |

| Em | G7 | D | G | G ‖

Verse 3

C   Am7
  If you look under the bed,

          D7   G
Then you can see my house from here.

C   A7
  So just lie against the wall,

          D7   G
Watch my conscience disappear now baby.

Chorus 3

Em
  Yeah, I'll be around when he's not in town, oh,

C
  Yeah, I'll show you how you're doing it wrong, oh,

Em
  I really love it when you tell me to stop, oh,

D   G
  Oh, it's turning me on.

Outro

Em
  I only come here 'cause I know it makes you sad,

C
  I only do it 'cause I know you know it's bad.

                Em
Oh don't you know that it's ugly and it shouldn't be like that?

          D   G
Oh, but, oh it's turning me on.

| C7 | A7 D7 | G ‖

Something Changed

Music by Pulp
Lyrics by Jarvis Cocker

G   Gsus4   G2   Bm   C   D   E   Am7   Dsus4

Intro ‖: G   Gsus4 G   G2 | G   Gsus4 G   :‖

Verse 1
G   Bm   C
   I wrote this song two hours before we met,
G   Bm   C
   I didn't know your name or what you looked like yet.
       D   Bm   E
I could have stayed at home and gone to bed,
C   D   Bm   E
   I could have gone to see a film instead.
Bm   E   Am7   D
   You might have changed your mind and seen your friends,
Bm   E   Am7   D
   Life could have been very diff'rent but then
Am7   D   Dsus4   D
   Something changed.

‖: G   Gsus4 G   G2 | G   Gsus4 G   :‖

Verse 2
                   Bm   C
  Do you believe that there's someone up above?
G   Bm   C
   And does he have a timetable directing acts of love?
       D   Bm   E
Why did I write this song on that one day?
C   D   Bm   E
   Why did you touch my hand and softly say
Bm   E   Am7 D
   "Stop asking questions that don't matter any - way,
Bm   E   Am7   D
   Just give us a kiss to celebrate here today."
Am7   D   Dsus4   D
   Something changed.

```
| G    Gsus4 G   G2 | G    Gsus4 G        ‖
```

Instrumental ‖: G | G | Bm | C   :‖

Verse 3

        C   D
When we woke up that morning
     Bm   E
We had no way of knowing,
         C   D
That in a matter of hours
    Bm   E
We'd change the way we were going,
Bm   E
  Where would I be now?
Bm   E
  Where would I be now
    Am7 D
If we'd never met?
Bm   E
  Would I be singing this song
  Am7   D
To someone else instead?
    Am7   D   Dsus4 D
I don't know, but like you just said,
G
  Something changed.

Sorted For E's & Wizz

Music by Pulp
Lyrics by Jarvis Cocker

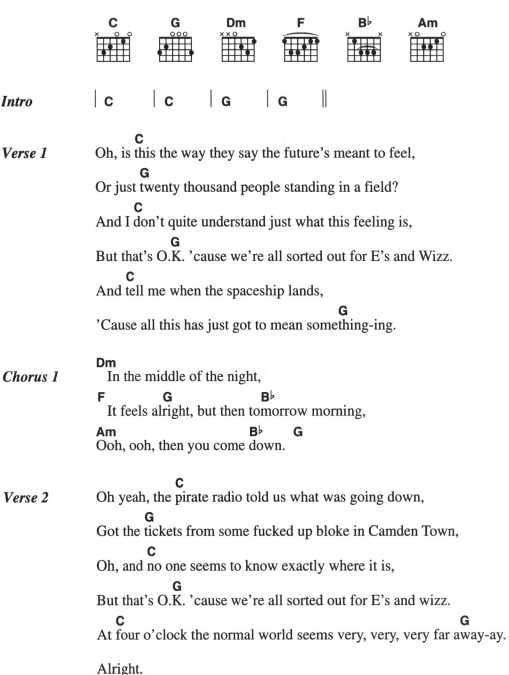

Intro | C | C | G | G ‖

Verse 1
        C
Oh, is this the way they say the future's meant to feel,
   G
Or just twenty thousand people standing in a field?
   C
And I don't quite understand just what this feeling is,
        G
But that's O.K. 'cause we're all sorted out for E's and Wizz.
   C
And tell me when the spaceship lands,
                G
'Cause all this has just got to mean something-ing.

Chorus 1
  Dm
  In the middle of the night,
F   **G**   **B♭**
  It feels alright, but then tomorrow morning,
Am   **B♭** **G**
Ooh, ooh, then you come down.

Verse 2
       C
Oh yeah, the pirate radio told us what was going down,
   G
Got the tickets from some fucked up bloke in Camden Town,
   C
Oh, and no one seems to know exactly where it is,
   G
But that's O.K. 'cause we're all sorted out for E's and wizz.
 C   **G**
At four o'clock the normal world seems very, very, very far away-ay.

Alright.

Chorus 2   As Chorus 1

                                C   **G**

Verse 3   Just keep on moving.

              C

              Everybody asks your name, they say we're all the same,

                    G

              And now it's "Nice-one, geezer,"

              But that's as far as conversation went.

               C

              I lost my friends, I dance alone, it's six o'clock, I wanna go home,

              G

               It's "No way," "Not today," makes you wonder what it meant.

               C

               And this feeling grows,

              And grows and grows and grows,

                    G

              And you want to call your mother and say,

              "Mother, can I never come home again

               C

               'Cause I seem to have left an important part of my brain somewhere,

              G

               Somewhere in a field in Hampshire."

              Alright.

              Dm

Chorus 3   In the middle of the night,

              F   **G**   **B♭**

               It feels alright, but then tomorrow morning,

              Am   **B♭**

              Ooh, ooh, then you come down.

              Am   **B♭**

              Ooh, ooh, then you come down.

              Am   **B♭**

              Ooh, what if you never come down?

Underwear

Music by Pulp
Lyrics by Jarvis Cocker

[Chord diagrams: A, C#7, D, Dm, F#m, E, G#7sus4, G#7, Asus4]

Verse 1

    A   C#7   D
Why don't you shut the door and close the curtains,
    Dm
'Cause you're not going anywhere.
A   C#7   D
He's coming up the stairs and in a moment
     Dm
He'll want to see your underwear.

Chorus 1

D   Dm   A
I couldn't stop it now, there's no way to get out,
      F#m   E
He's standing far too near, and how the hell did you get here,
      F#m   D   A
Semi-naked in somebody else's room?
         F#m   E
I'd give my whole life to see it,
    D   Dm   A
Just you stood there only in your underwear.

Verse 2

                    C#7   D
If fashion is your trade, then when you're naked,
    Dm
I guess you must be unemployed, yeah.
A   C#7   D
But once it's under way there's no escaping
     Dm
The fact that you're a girl and he's a boy.

Chorus 2   As Chorus 1

Instrumental ‖: A | G#7sus4 G#7 | Asus4 A | E G#7 :‖
                   | A | C#7 | D | Dm ‖

Verse 3

```
        A                    C#7         D
    If you could close your eyes and just remember
        Dm
That this is what you wanted last night.
    A              C#7         D
    So why is it so hard for you to touch him,
                  Dm
For you to go, give yourself to him? Oh Jesus.
```

Chorus 2   As Chorus 1

Instrumental   ‖: A | G#7sus4   G#7 | Asus4   A | E   G#7 :‖

Outro

```
    A                      G#7sus4  G#7
    Do, do, do, do, do, do,      do,
Asus4  A    E    G#7
Do,   do,  do. _____
    A                      G#7sus4  G#7
    Do, do, do, do, do, do,      do,
Asus4  A    E    G#7  A
Do,   do,  do. _____
        C#7            D
Oh yeah, I wanna see you,
            Dm                         A
Wanna see you standing in your underwear.
```

Pink Glove

Music by Pulp
Lyrics by Jarvis Cocker

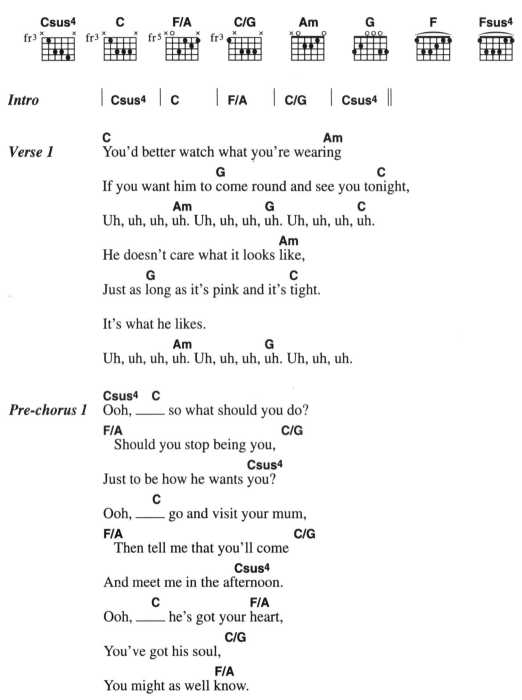

Intro　　　| Csus⁴ | C　　| F/A | C/G | Csus⁴ ‖

Verse 1

C
You'd better watch what you're wearing
　　　　　　　　　　　　　　　　　　　Am

G　　　　　　　　　　　　　　　　　　C
If you want him to come round and see you tonight,
Am　　　　　G　　　　　C
Uh, uh, uh, uh. Uh, uh, uh, uh. Uh, uh, uh, uh.
　　　　　　　　　　　　　　　Am
He doesn't care what it looks like,
G　　　　　　　　　　C
Just as long as it's pink and it's tight.

It's what he likes.
　　　　　　　Am　　　　　　G
Uh, uh, uh, uh. Uh, uh, uh, uh. Uh, uh, uh.

Pre-chorus 1

Csus⁴　C
Ooh, ＿＿＿ so what should you do?
F/A　　　　　　　　　　　　　C/G
　Should you stop being you,
　　　　　　　　　　　Csus⁴
Just to be how he wants you?
　　　　　C
Ooh, ＿＿＿ go and visit your mum,
F/A　　　　　　　　　　　　　C/G
　Then tell me that you'll come
　　　　　　　　　　　Csus⁴
And meet me in the afternoon.
　　　　　C　　　　　F/A
Ooh, ＿＿＿ he's got your heart,
　　　　　　　　　　C/G
You've got his soul,
　　　　　　　　　F/A
You might as well know.

Chorus 1

```
              G                 C
I know you're never gonna be with me,
            Am               G          F
But do you understand now that maybe you got it right first time?
      G                 C
I realise that you'll never leave him,
            Am               G                    F
But every now and then in the evening, you could get it right first time.
              G                 C
And I know you think I've got to be joking,
            Am                       G
But if you touch him again then I'm going,
                 F
Oh, you got it right first time,
Fsus4   F          Csus4  C  F/A  C/G
   Get it right first time.
```

Verse 2

```
 C                                         Am
  And now you've done it once, now he wants you
    G                       C
To wear your pink glove all the time.
        Am          G
Uh, uh, uh, uh. Uh, uh, uh, uh. Uh, uh, uh, uh.
```

Pre-chorus 2   As Pre-chorus 1

Chorus 2

```
              G                 C
I know you're never gonna be with me,
            Am               G          F
But do you understand now that maybe you got it right first time?
      G                 C
I realise that you'll never leave him,
            Am               G                    F
But every now and then in the evening, you could get it right first time.
              G                 C
And I know you think I've got to be joking,
            Am                       G
But if you touch him again then I'm going,
                 F
Oh, you got it right first time,
Fsus4       F          C
   You got it right first time, oh, oh, oh, oh.
```

Verse 3

(C)
Oh, you'll always be together
      Am   G
'Cos he gets you up in leather
         C
And you know what to wear at the end of the day,
      Am   G
And I'd laugh if I saw but I'm out of the way.
         C
Yeah, it's too long ago, shouldn't care anymore,
      Am   G
But I wanted to know, is it as good as before?
         C
Yeah, it's hard to believe that you'd go for that stuff,
      Am ·   G
All those baby-doll nighties, synthetic fluff,
         C
Oh, it looks pretty good, yeah, it fits you O.K., yeah,
Am   G   F
Wear your pink glove, babe, he put it on the wrong way.

Chorus 3

              G   C
I know you're never gonna be with me,
         Am   G   F
But do you understand now that maybe you got it right first time?
     G   C
I realise that you'll never leave him,
         Am   G   F
But every now and then in the evening, you could get it right first time.
             G   C
And I know you think I've got to be joking,
         Am   G
But if you touch him again then I'm going,
         F
Oh, you got it right first time.
           G   C
Yeah, oh, I know that you'll never leave him,
         Am   G
Uh, uh, uh, uh, but you see him,
         Fsus4   E
You got it right first ti-ime,
Fsus4   F   C
   Got it right first time.

Printed and bound in Great Britain by
Caligraving Limited Thetford Norfolk